and then circle those animals that still need to find a twin.

Illustration: Scott Peck

AUNT ADA

Aunt Ada is very particular. She likes only certain things on certain days. Can you look at each group below and figure out what she likes about one set of numbers?

FRIDAY

Aunt Ada likes:	Aunt Ada doesn't like:
1, 2, 3, 9	7, 11, 98, 13

THURSDAY

Aunt Ada likes:	Aunt Ada doesn't like:
8, 11, 18	7, 12, 17

WEDNESDAY

Aunt Ada likes:	Aunt Ada doesn't like:
1, 2, 10, 6	3, 4, 12, 9

TUESDAY

Aunt Ada likes:	Aunt Ada doesn't like:
12, 45, 89	11, 22, 44

MONDAY

Aunt Ada likes:	Aunt Ada doesn't like:
2, 8, 24, 16	3, 17, 55, 31

Hint on page 46

Answer on page 48

Illustration: Marc Nadel

PAIR SQUARES

The numbers from 1 to 9 belong on these cupcakes. The trick is that each pair of cupcakes should add up to the number inside the square pan they touch.

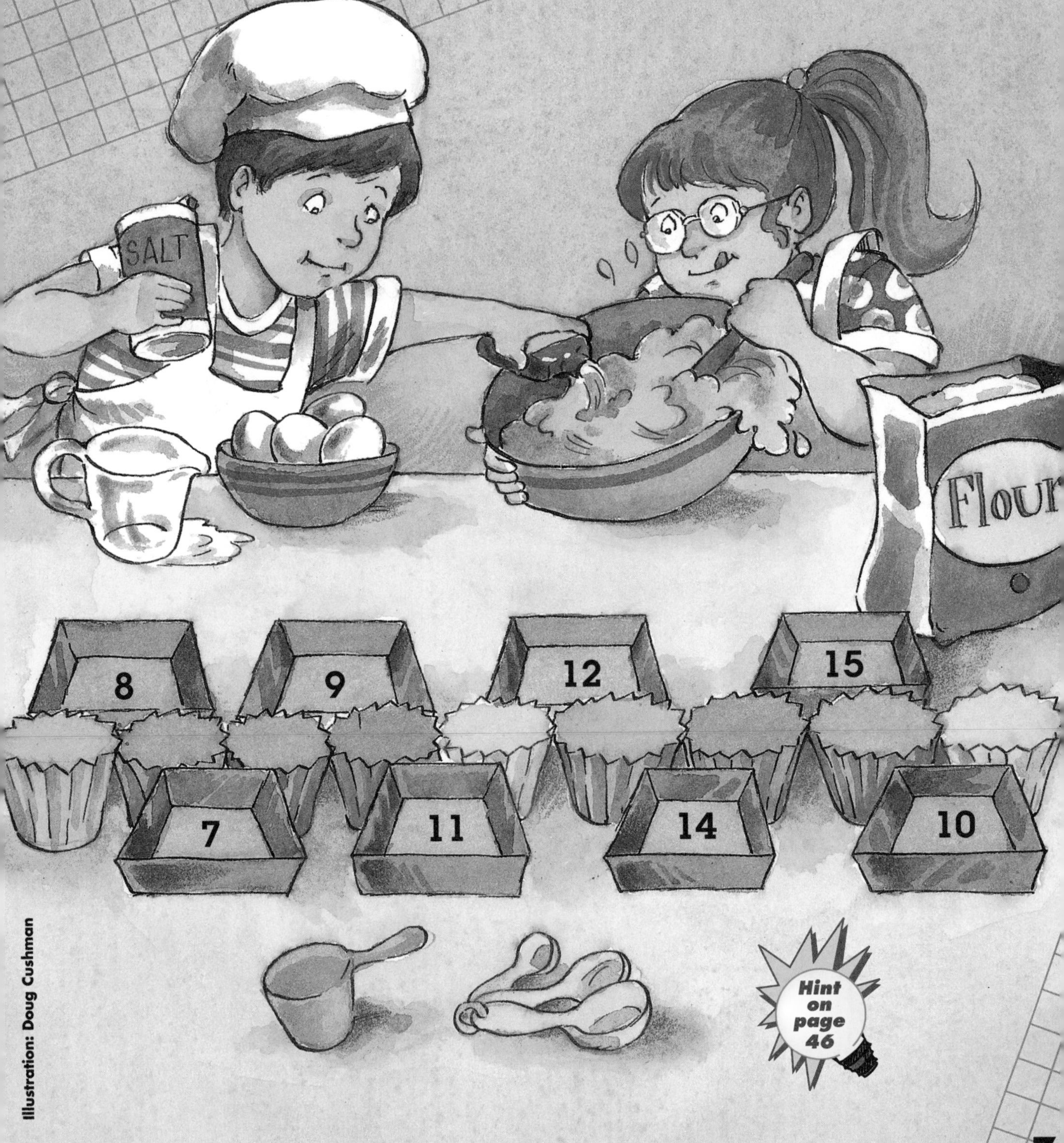

SALT
Flour
8
9
12
15
7
11
14
10
Hint on page 46

Illustration: Doug Cushman

Answer on page 48

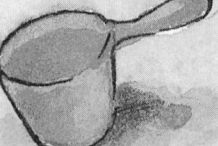

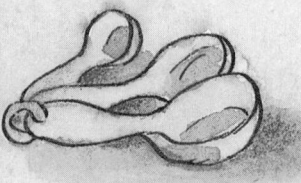

DANCING DIGITS

Answer on page 48

with the description
on one of the cards?

I. My tens place is double my ones place number.

A. You can write my digits backward and I still equal the same number.

J. I equal $\frac{1}{9}$ of letter I or $\frac{1}{7}$ of letter E.

B. I equal 2 dozen.

K. I am divisible by 1, 3, 6, and 9.

C. I have a 4 in my ones place.

D. I am $\frac{1}{4}$ of letter B above.

L. I am the highest number here.

E. You can find me by adding H and B together.

M. If you multiply my tens number by my ones number, you will get $\frac{1}{2}$ of letter D.

F. I am $\frac{1}{5}$ of 25.

N. I am worth more when added to any other number than when multiplied by it.

G. I am the lowest even number here.

O. I am worth twice D, but only $\frac{1}{2}$ of B.

H. I am 5 times larger than F.

Hint on page 46

Illustration: Diana Zourelias

CHUCKERS

How much wood could a woodchuck chuck if a woodchuck could chuck wood?

A. Wally Woodchuck is chucking wood at the speed of 65 pieces per minute. How many pieces will he chuck in 5 minutes?

B. Wendy Woodchuck has 8 minutes to chuck aside 360 pieces. At what average speed will she work to chuck them all in time?

C. Wampus Woodchuck must move 810 pieces. His top chucking speed is 90 pieces a minute. How much time will he need to complete the job?

Illustration: David Helton

Answer on page 48

DOTS A LOT

Count by 4s to connect the dots and reveal something with real horsepower.

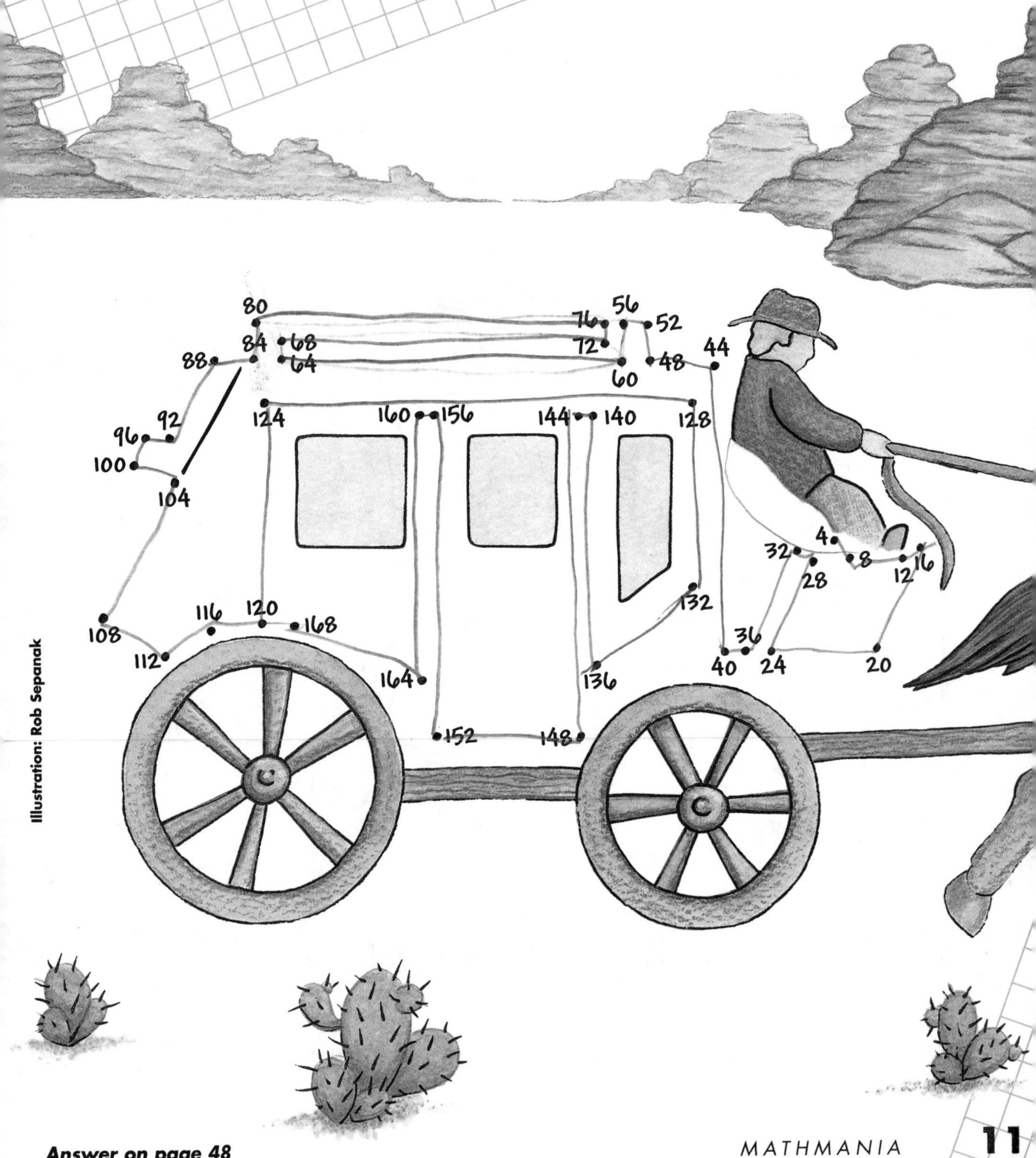

Illustration: Rob Sepanak

80
84 • 68
88 • 64
92
96
100
104
124
160 • 156
144 • 140
128
76 • 56 52
72 • 48 44
60
4
32 • 8
28 12 16
108 116 120 168
112 164
132
36
40 24 20
152 148 136

FAMILY MATTERS

Answer on page 48

Hint on page 46

Illustration: Bill Colrus

figure out the number of people in her family. Can you help?

Fran's grandparents on her father's side had two children, a boy and a girl. Each of them married and had two children.

Fran's grandparents on her mother's side also had two children, both girls. Each of them married and had two children.

Can you figure out the number of relatives Fran has in each category?

Grandparents: 4   Aunts: 2

Parents: 2   First Cousins: 4

Uncles: 2   Siblings: 1

HOUSE HUNTING

Can you use the clues to identify which house in this cul-de-sac Reba Rental just sold?

Hint on page 46

Answer on page 48

The Clements live farther north than the Edgerlys.

The Edgerlys live farther west than the Pattons.

The Jacobs live northeast of the Springers and northwest of the Pattons.

The Springers are on the opposite side of the Pattons and northwest of the Edgerlys.

Reba just sold the Clements' place.

Which house is it?

BIRD WORDS

Write the name of each bird on the blanks next to it. Then write the letters on the blanks with the matching numbers to find the answer to the riddle below.

$\overline{1}$ $\overline{2}$ $\overline{3}$ $\overline{4}$ $\overline{5}$

$\overline{3}$ $\overline{6}$ $\overline{7}$ $\overline{8}$ $\overline{9}$ $\overline{10}$ $\overline{11}$

$\overline{12}$ $\overline{10}$ $\overline{1}$ $\overline{1}$ $\overline{2}$ $\overline{13}$

$\overline{14}$ $\overline{12}$ $\overline{10}$ $\overline{1}$ $\overline{1}$ $\overline{2}$ $\overline{15}$

$\overline{16}$ $\overline{7}$ $\overline{17}$ $\overline{17}$ $\overline{4}$ $\overline{5}$ $\overline{18}$ $\overline{3}$ $\overline{4}$ $\overline{1}$ $\overline{19}$

Why is the sky so high?

$\overline{14}$ $\overline{2}$ $\overline{3}$ $\overline{4}$ $\overline{1}$ $\overline{19}$ $\overline{14}$ $\overline{15}$ $\overline{2}$ $\overline{5}$ $\overline{13}$

$\overline{3}$ $\overline{7}$ $\overline{17}$ $\overline{12}$ $\overline{13}$ $\overline{16}$ $\overline{8}$ $\overline{4}$ $\overline{1}$ $\overline{16}$ $\overline{8}$ $\overline{10}$ $\overline{19}$ $\overline{14}$

Answer on page 48

MATH MAZE

A number of paths lead through this maze, but only one is the right path. To find it, solve each problem.

START

17 − 15

2 + 2

25 ÷ 25

12 ÷ 4

12 ÷ 3

16 ÷ 2

42 ÷ 2

3 + 2

11 − 3

LETTUCE

3 × 2

21 ÷ 3

5 + 4

7 × 2

6 × 2

5 + 6

5 × 4

5 × 2

9 + 3

15 − 4

5 × 4

3 × 3

17 + 1

30 ÷ 2

4 × 4

8 + 5

2 × 7

24 − 5

19 + 9

3 × 6

18 ÷ 2

6 × 2

15 − 7

15 + 2

Then find the path that has the
answers following in sequence,
beginning with 1.

6 × 4

5 × 5

30 − 7

14 + 8

6 × 0

18 + 8

30 − 2

15 + 6

30 − 3

4 × 7

20 + 7

21 + 8

48 ÷ 6

3 × 10

9 × 3

21 + 10

16 + 16

8 × 4

39 − 6

17 × 2

8 × 5

3 × 11

40 − 9

7 × 5

18 + 9

6 × 6

FINISH

LISTEN UP

Each word posted here belongs on one of the train cars. To find out which word goes where, solve the problems on the cars. Then match each answer to one of the numbers above a word. Put that word on the matching car. The first one is done for you.

6	12	18	24	30
A	ITS	HEAR?	BY	HOW

34	38	42	46	50
ENGINE-	CAN	USING	TRAIN	EARS

16 + 14 = 30 __How__

41 − 3 = _____

2 × 3 = _____

31 + 15 = _____

36 ÷ 2 = _____

4 × 6 = _____

49 − 7 = _____

48 ÷ 4 = _____

18 + 16 = _____

5 × 10 = _____

Illustration: Rick Geary

INDIVISIBLE

The words below make up a very well known statement. But the words are listed based on the number of letters in each word. Use the lists to answer the questions about the words.

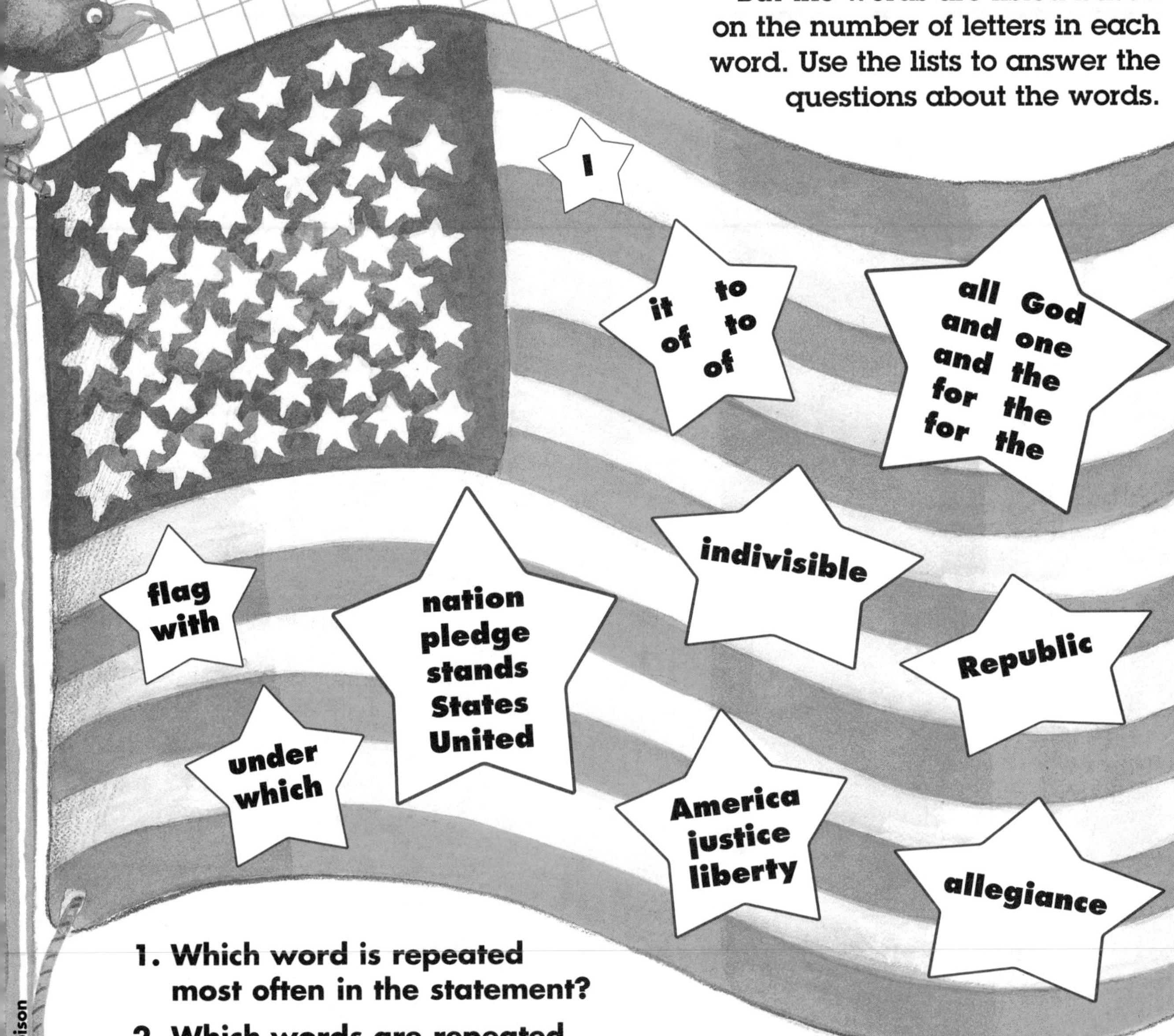

I

it to
of to
of

all God
and one
and the
for the
for the

indivisible

flag
with

nation
pledge
stands
States
United

Republic

under
which

America
justice
liberty

allegiance

1. **Which word is repeated most often in the statement?**

2. **Which words are repeated the second-most often?**

3. **Which word has one letter repeated four times?**

4. **In the statement, there are words of every size, from one letter to eleven letters, except one. Which size is missing?**

5. **How many words of three letters or more begin and end with the same letter?**

> **Now, can you put the words in the right order to read the statement?**

Answer on page 49

Illustration: Don Robison

SCRAMBLED PICTURE

Copy these mixed-up rectangles onto the next page to unscramble the scene.

A-3
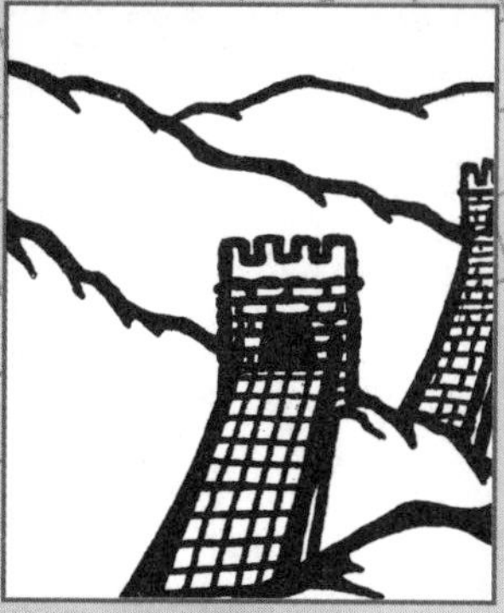
A-1
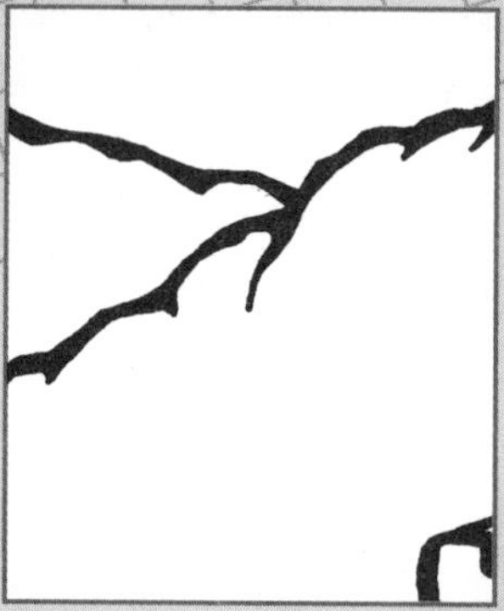
A-4
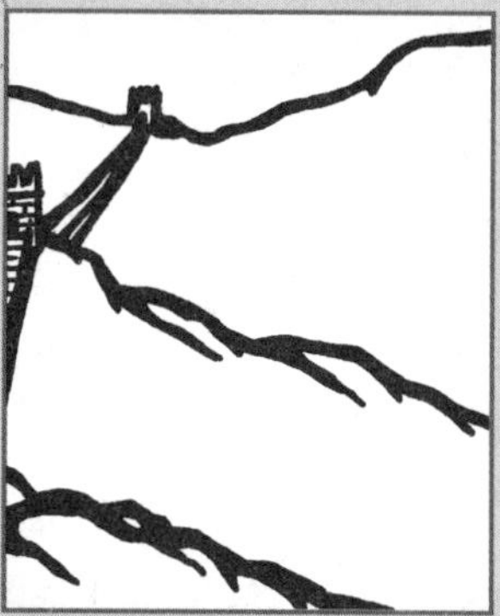
A-2
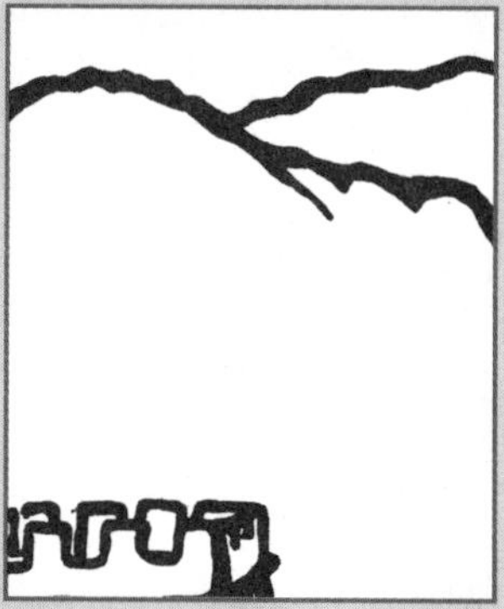
B-2
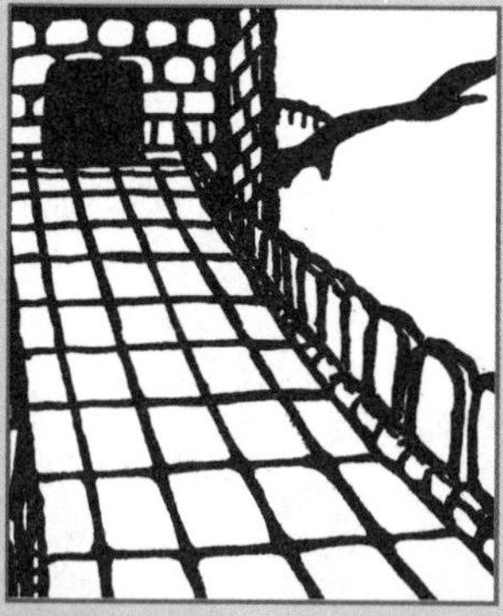
B-4
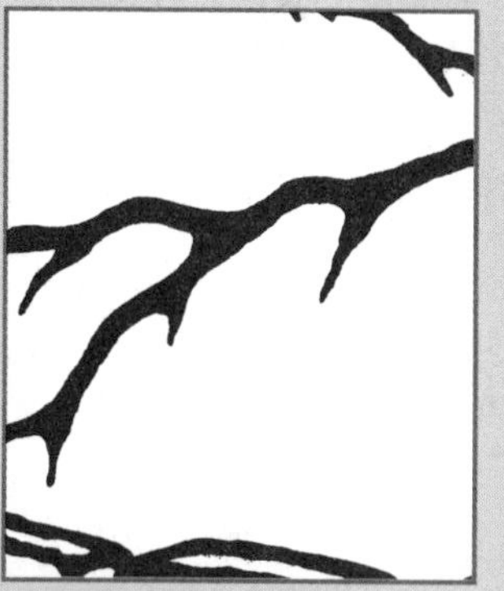
B-3
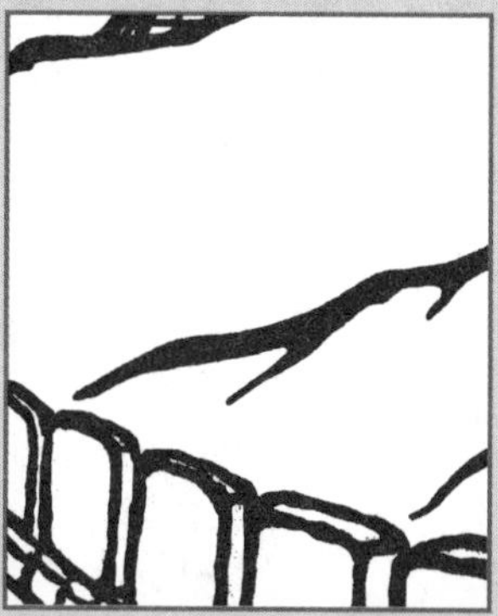
B-1
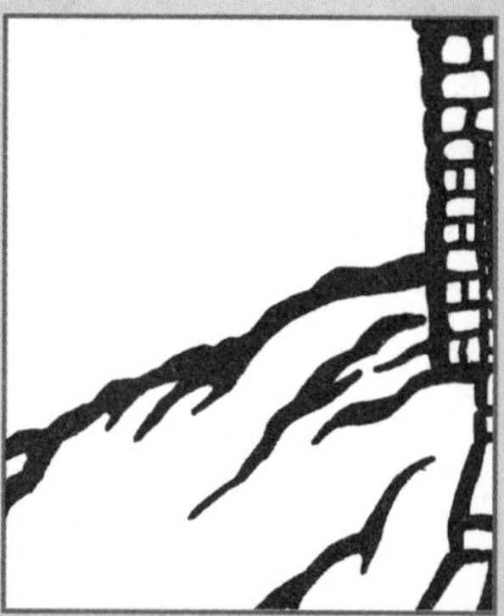
C-4
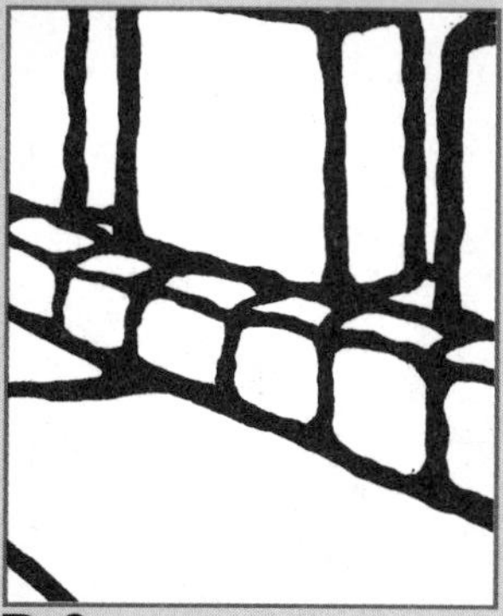
C-3
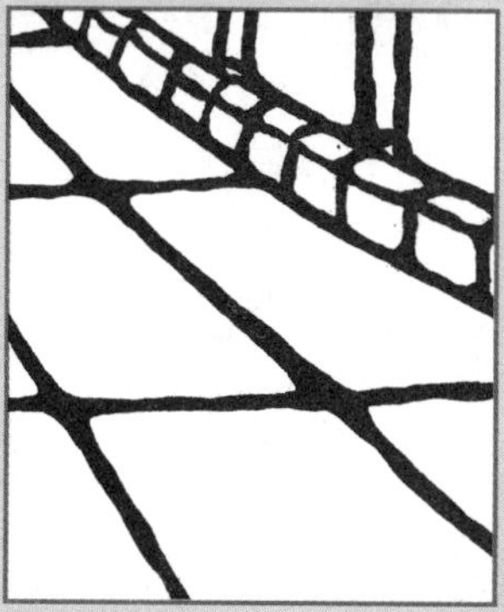
C-1
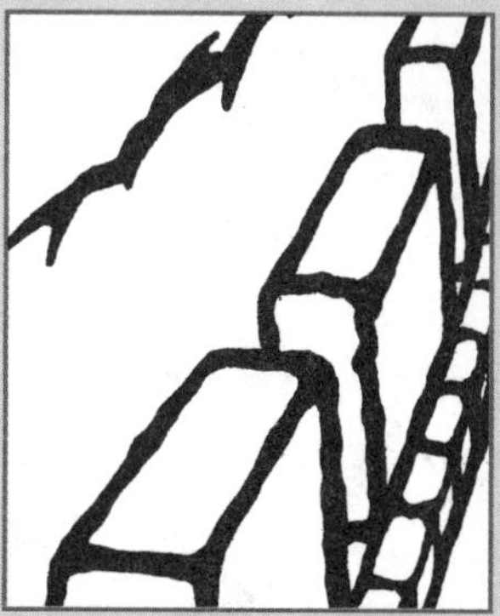
C-2
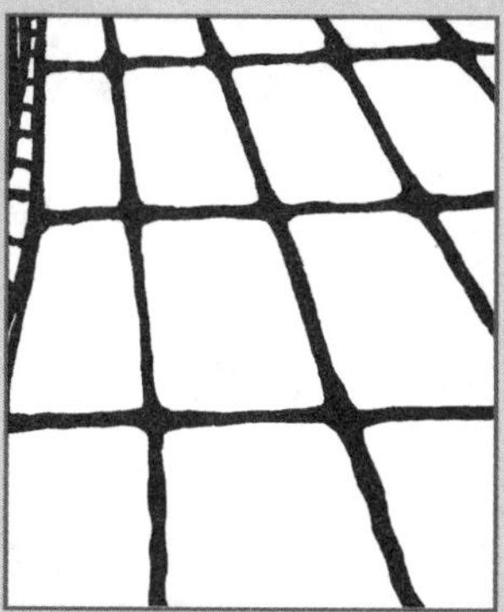
D-3
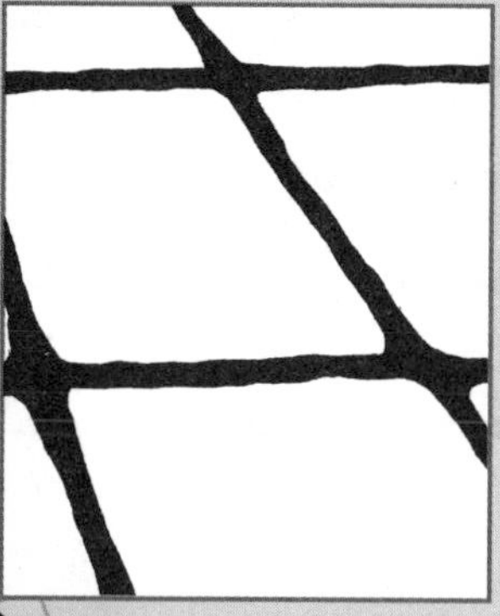
D-1
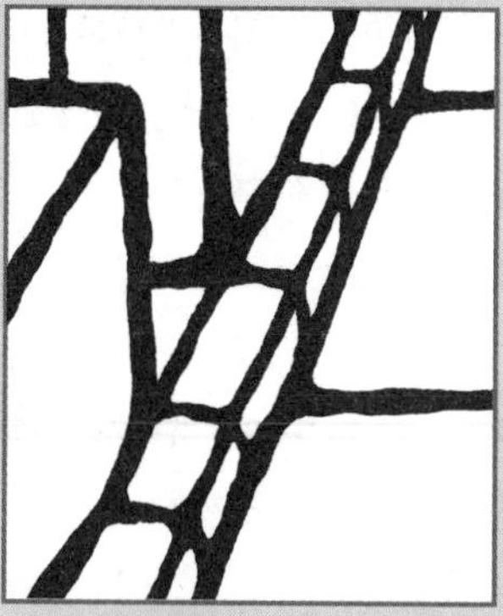
D-4
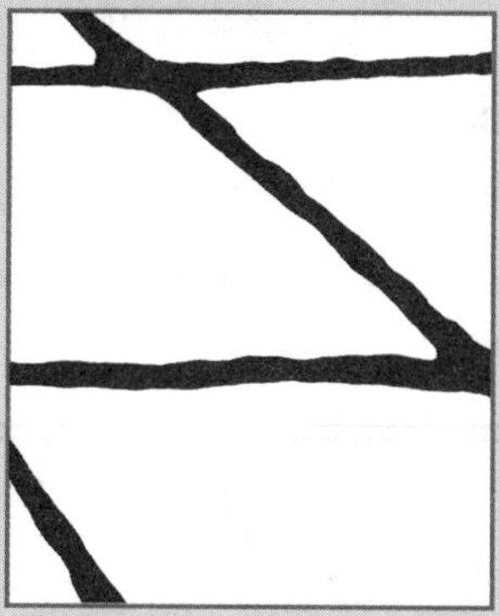
D-2
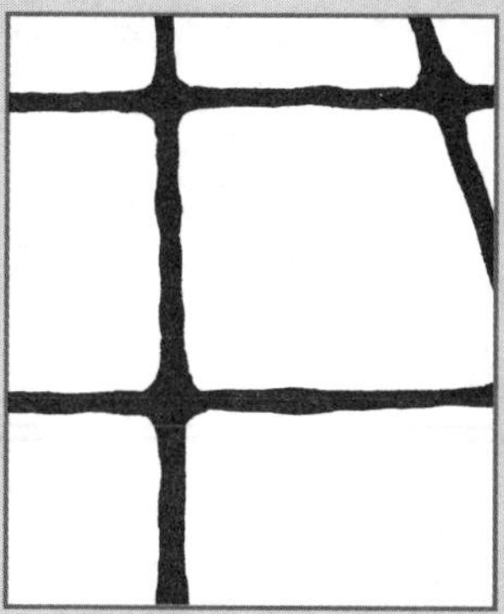

The letters and numbers tell you where each rectangle belongs. We've done the first one, A-3, to start you off.

1 2 3 4

A B C D

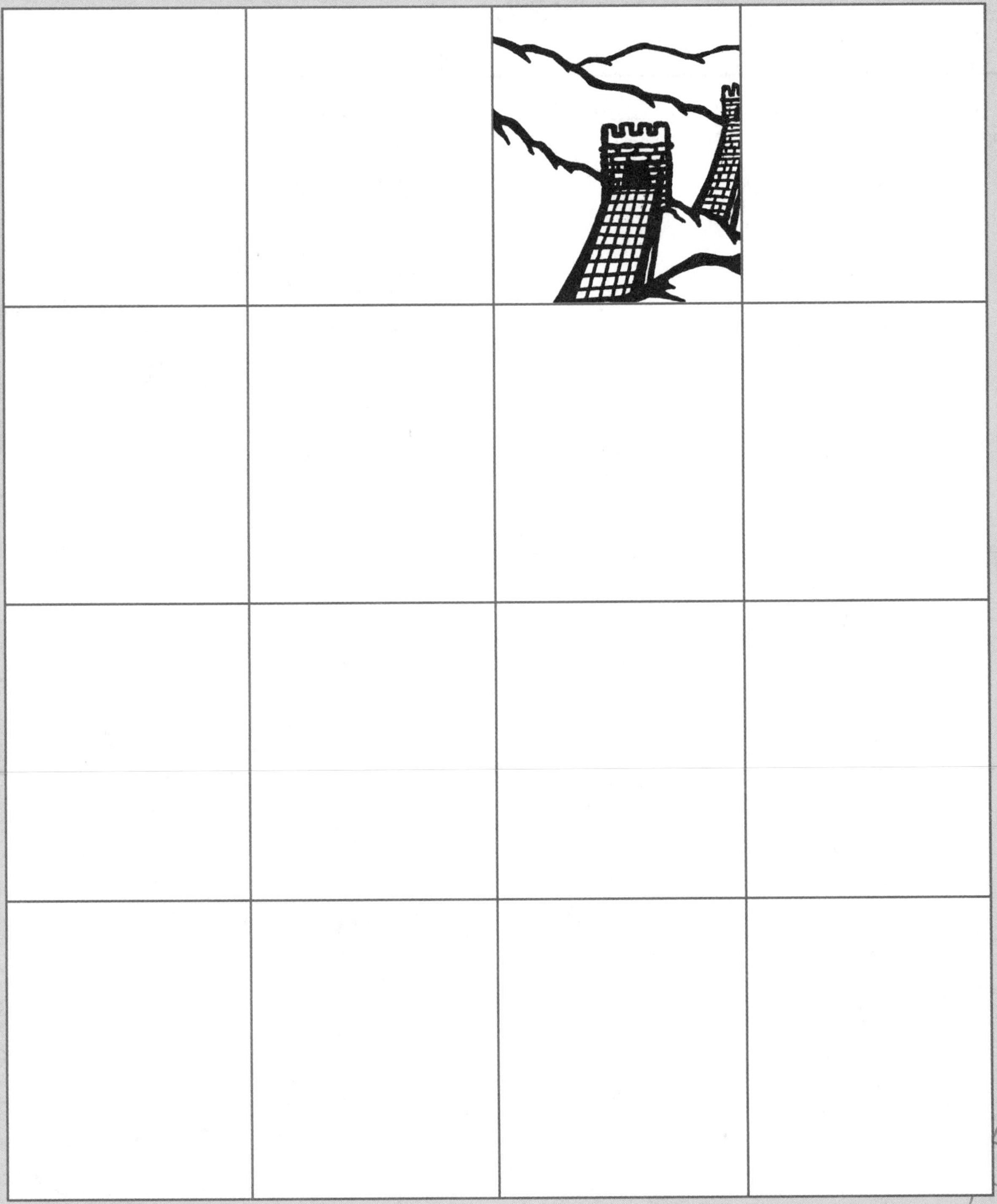

Illustration: Rob Sepanak

Answer on page 49

TALENT NIGHT

Hint on page 46

Some talented students performed at this year's Open School Night. Miss Palmer, the show's coordinator, had a tough time keeping track of who went on when. Still, everyone managed to appear on time, and the show was a big success. Now Miss Palmer is trying to write a recap of the show. From the clues here, can you help her remember who went on at what time?

1. Manuel performed his magic show at either 8:00 or 9:00.
2. Tanya went on a half-hour after Sylvia, but a half-hour before Manuel.
3. Desiree twirled her baton at one of the half-hour times.
4. Gil played the banjo one hour before Sylvia performed.

TIMES

7:00 _____
7:30 _____
8:00 _____
8:30 _____
9:00 _____

Illustration: R. Michael Palan

Answer on page 49

HIDDEN MEASURES

A unit of measurement is hidden in each sentence. The letters in each word will appear in order, though they may be spread between two or more words. The sentences may act as clues to the hidden words. Can you measure up to the challenge of finding all 15 words?

1. They prefer to make small measurements in China.

2. Mac really wanted that piece of land.

3. Doubt caused Stephanie to uncertainly measure the fruit.

4. Bryce left his car at the jewelry store.

5. The elephant was too big to notice how much he ate.

6. Emil explained that he was tired from the long drive.

7. The actress smiled and said, "My ardent fans know I have three feet when I dance."

8. I ate the ice cream that was up in the freezer.

9. The bus held enough fruit for everyone.

10. We let the flag unfurl on Grand Race Day.

11. Let's not rush our time together.

12. It won't take long to tell you why my house is in worse condition than yours.

13. This road is measured for odd lengths.

14. I saw that gal long before you finished the milk.

15. Is Eric up getting the coffee?

Hint on page 46

Answer on page 49

CROSSNUMBER

Answer each question as you would in a regular crossword, and then place the numbers into the grid, one number per box.

ACROSS

1. Year of America's independence
4. Halloween always falls on this date.
6. 2 dozen minus 2
7. One thousand five hundred twenty-one
9. Number of years in a millennium
10. Number of cards in a standard deck
12. Years in $5\frac{1}{2}$ decades
14. 6000 – 90
17. Pounds in a ton
18. Number of years in a decade
19. Four score
20. How eleven o'clock appears on a digital clock

DOWN

1. How a quarter after twelve appears on a digital clock
2. Hours in 3 days
3. Minutes in 10 hours and 10 minutes
4. $35.00 – $2.95
5. 1 inch less than a foot is ___ inches.
8. Number of United States
11. $\frac{1}{4}$ of 10,000
13. Number of pounds in $2\frac{1}{2}$ tons
15. A decade less than a century
16. Number of Dalmatians in a famous book
17. 2 × 14
18. A perfect score in gymnastics

Answer on page 49

Hint on page 46

Illustration: Rick Geary

25

SNOW PROBLEM

Shyniqua is shoveling snow from driveways to make some extra money. She charges people by the foot-length of the property shoveled. Can you help her figure out the length of a house lot and a parking lot?

Answer on page 49

Three house lots and one driveway are as long as a parking lot.

Two driveways are as long as one house lot.

A parking lot is seven times longer than a driveway.

Three and one-half house lots will fit into a parking lot.

Each driveway is 100 feet long.

Hint on page 46

Illustration: R. Michael Palan

SQUARE DIVISION

Using only four lines, divide this square to make the greatest number of sections possible.

Illustration: John Nez

Answer on page 49

Hint on page 47

A VINE TIME

Each vine sprouts one leaf for every 6 inches of growth. Can you tell how long each vine is in feet?

Answer on page 50

Hint on page 47

Illustration: Rick Geary

MATHMAGIC

Put a dime, a nickel, and four pennies in one pocket.

Ask a friend if she has a penny. As she pulls out the coin, you pull out your coins and rattle them in your hand **WITHOUT SHOWING THE COINS.**

Then tell your friend this: "You have a single penny, which is an odd coin. If we add it to all the money in my hand, will all of it together be odd or even?"

No matter what your friend guesses, she will be wrong.

"Coin" you figure out how this one works?

PRECISE ICE

Can you redraw this figure without crossing over or going back along any lines?

Illustration: Barbara Gray

Answer on page 50

ANACROSTIC

Write the answers to the clues on the numbered blanks. Some clues ask for word answers, which can be spelled out one letter per blank. Other clues ask for number answers, which can also be spelled out on the blanks.

A. 2 + 2 + 2 + 2 + 2 + 2 + 2:

$\overline{27}$ $\overline{35}$ $\overline{19}$ $\overline{42}$ $\overline{2}$ $\overline{53}$ $\overline{23}$ $\overline{12}$

B. Ice or roller:

$\overline{24}$ $\overline{5}$ $\overline{4}$ $\overline{43}$ $\overline{45}$

C. Number after 999,999 (2 words):

$\overline{48}$ $\overline{31}$ $\overline{9}$ $\overline{18}$ $\overline{41}$ $\overline{52}$ $\overline{22}$ $\overline{51}$ $\overline{17}$ $\overline{46}$

D. Definitely needed, I ____ have that:

$\overline{50}$ $\overline{33}$ $\overline{7}$ $\overline{13}$

E. 6 + 5 + 4 + 3 + 2:

$\overline{3}$ $\overline{16}$ $\overline{11}$ $\overline{36}$ $\overline{47}$ $\overline{38}$

F. Person in charge of a project or job:

$\overline{32}$ $\overline{26}$ $\overline{20}$ $\overline{49}$

G. 90 ÷ 3:

$\overline{34}$ $\overline{40}$ $\overline{1}$ $\overline{28}$ $\overline{15}$ $\overline{14}$

H. The price of something:

$\overline{21}$ $\overline{29}$ $\overline{8}$ $\overline{39}$

I. 48 − 36:

$\overline{25}$ $\overline{30}$ $\overline{6}$ $\overline{37}$ $\overline{10}$ $\overline{44}$

Then take each letter from its blank and put it into the matching numbered square on the grid. Work back and forth between the grid and the word list to fill all the spaces. Black squares separate words. When you are done, read from left to right to find a number-related fact.

1	2	■	3	4	5	6	7
■	8	9	10	11	12	13	14
—	15	16	17	■	18	19	20
21	22	23	24	■	25	26	■
27	28	29	30	31	■	32	33
34	■	35	36	37	38	■	39
40	41	42	43	44	45	46	■
47	48	■	49	50	51	52	53

Answer on page 50

Hint on page 47

33

HIDDEN NUMBERS

The answer to each problem is hidden somewhere in the grid. First solve each equation, working from left to right.

A. 281 × 2
B. 101 + 23 + 51
C. 2050 − 1225
D. 1776 + 1976
E. 120 × 10 + 50
F. 3 × 3 × 3 × 3 × 3
G. 10,765 + 45
H. 1492 + 2008
I. 5 × 111
J. 19,569 × 1
K. 2002 + 110
L. 7272 ÷ 2
M. 124 + 124

N. 1500 ÷ 10
O. 20 × 10 × 5 × 2
P. 1000 + 300 + 645 + 9
Q. 60,000 + 45,000 − 3005
R. 4000 × 2 + 95
S. 25,000 ÷ 5
T. 11 × 11
U. 4010 − 302
V. 650 + 50 + 20 + 11
W. 10,000 − 1430
X. 5000 + 100 + 9
Y. 5121 ÷ 3
Z. 6501 − 263

Answer on page 50

Then look for and circle the answers, which may be hidden across, up, down, backward, or diagonally.

```
    1 8        0 1
    5 3        0 8
    3 2        5 5
    0 6        3 7
2 4 8 5 3 7 3 1 6 0 0 3 4 2
5 5 1 9 5 4 8 6 2 1 1 2 0 6
    7 2 0 6 0 1
    5 9 9 1 0 1
1 9 5 6 9 5 5 0 0 0 6 9 0 8
3 7 5 2 9 1 5 5 4 8 0 7 3 8
    7 7        0 1
    0 5        5 0
    7 6        2 4
    1 2        1 7
```

Illustration: Jerry Zimmerman

35

SIMILAR CIRCLES

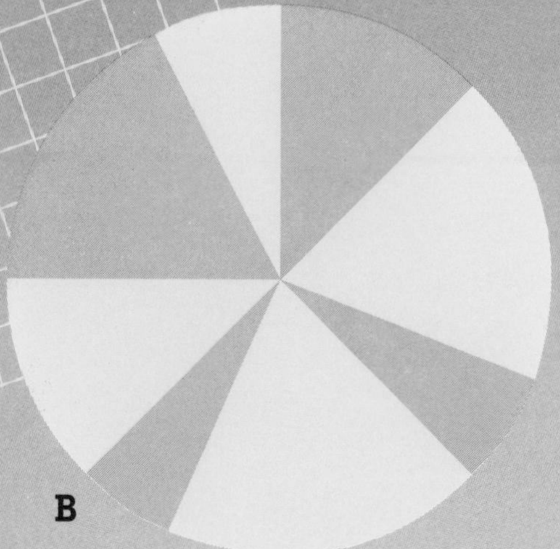

Can you tell which circle doesn't belong?

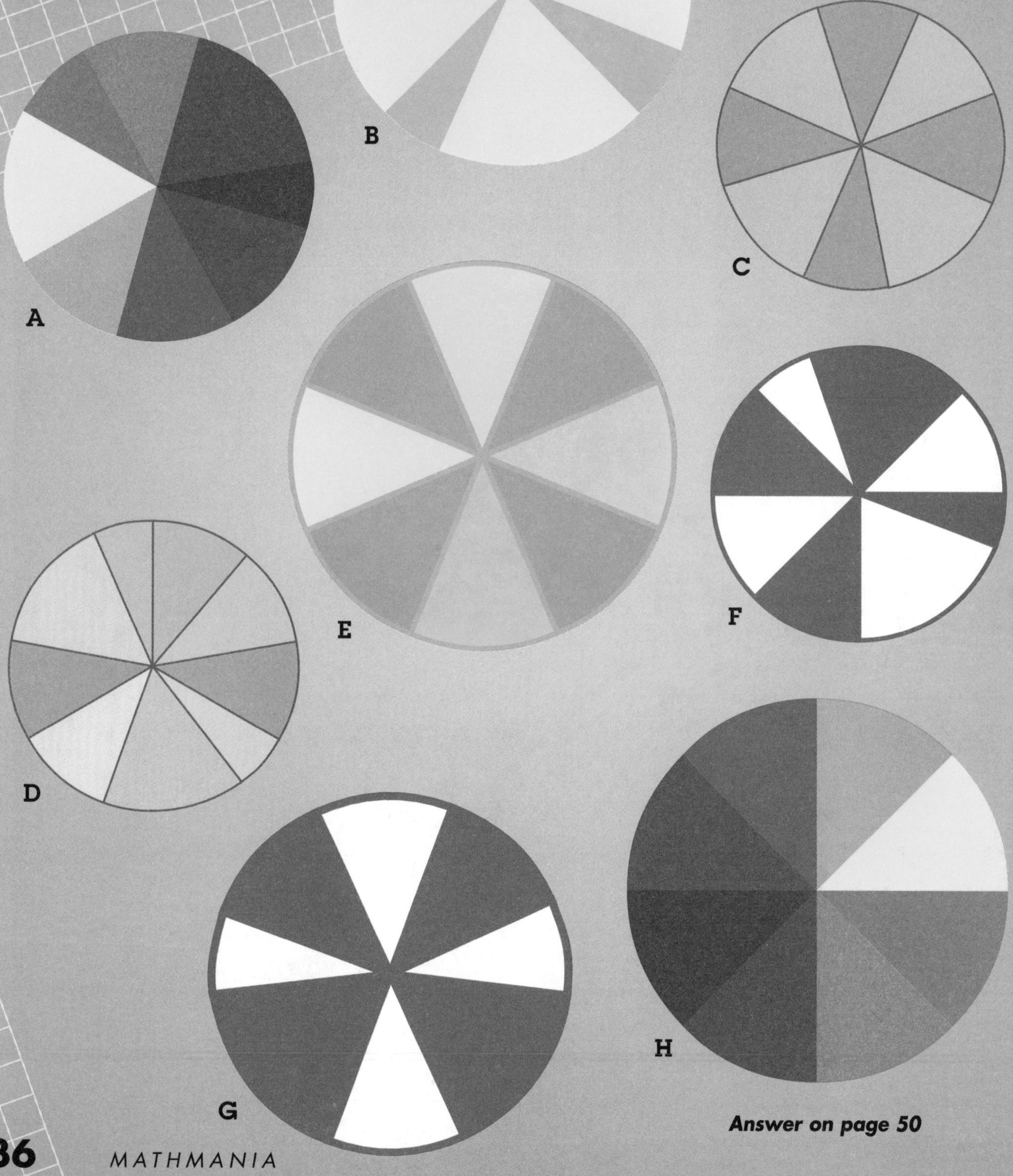

A

B

C

D

E

F

G

H

Answer on page 50

SCOUT SALES

The Giggle Scouts are just finishing up the annual cookie sales drive. Each scout is ready to turn in a final total of the boxes she sold. Can you tell which scout sold the most cookies and which scout earned the most money for the troop?

Illustration: R. Michael Palan

Hint on page 47

Answer on page 50

Aleesha
Ginger Snappies
@ $3.00 box—12 boxes
Crusty O Rings
@ $2.50 box—8 boxes
Coconutties
@ $3.25 box—12 boxes
Razzleberry Creams
@ $2.75 box—11 boxes

Bethany
Ginger Snappies
@ $3.00 box—15 boxes
Crusty O Rings
@ $2.50 box—10 boxes
Coconutties
@ $3.25 box—9 boxes
Razzleberry Creams
@ $2.75 box—6 boxes

Caitlin
Ginger Snappies
@ $3.00 box—3 boxes
Crusty O Rings
@ $2.50 box—13 boxes
Coconutties
@ $3.25 box—16 boxes
Razzleberry Creams
@ $2.75 box—10 boxes

Deandra
Ginger Snappies
@ $3.00 box—8 boxes
Crusty O Rings
@ $2.50 box—20 boxes
Coconutties
@ $3.25 box—7 boxes
Razzleberry Creams
@ $2.75 box—9 boxes

RHODES TRIP

This past summer, the Rhodes family set out to travel by camper from Tampa, Florida, to Seattle, Washington. When he returned

DIRECT TRIP

Tampa to Atlanta	455 miles
Atlanta to St. Louis	555 miles
St. Louis to Denver	860 miles
Denver to Billings	554 miles
Billings to Seattle	821 miles

SIDE TRIPS

Atlanta to Augusta	151 miles
Atlanta to Chicago	716 miles
St. Louis to Kansas City	256 miles

to school, B. Z. Rhodes wrote a report on the trip. Can you look at the mileage chart and the map to answer some of his questions?

Hint on page 47

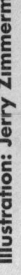

Illustration: Jerry Zimmerman

1. How many miles did the Rhodes family plan to travel round trip directly from Tampa to Seattle?

2. They drove at a constant speed of 65 miles per hour. How long did it take to get from Tampa to Atlanta?

3. While in Atlanta, they discussed a side trip to Augusta to see the famous Masters Tournament golf course. How many extra miles would that have added to their trip?

4. They didn't go to Augusta and thought about going from Atlanta directly to Chicago instead of Seattle. Had they done this, how many miles shorter would the entire trip have been?

5. Gas was $1.05 per gallon, and the camper got 20 miles to the gallon. How much did it cost to drive from St. Louis to Denver?

6. On this part of the trip, they averaged 64 mph and left St. Louis at 10:00 a.m. When did they arrive in Kansas City?

7. When they reached Denver, the Rhodeses were tired of traveling. They decided to stop and spend their vacation in Denver instead. How many miles did this save off their original plan?

LIBRARY LAUGHS

Dewey has some funny books in his library. To check one out, solve each problem. Then go to the shelves to find the volume with the number that matches each answer. Put the matching letter in the blank beside each answer. Read down the letters you've filled in to find the title and author of the book Dewey just finished reading.

Illustration: Scott Peck

Hint on page 47

Answer on page 51

$4 \times 5 =$ _____ _____
$12 + 6 =$ _____ _____
$12 - 11 =$ _____ _____
$11 \times 2 =$ _____ _____
$25 \div 5 =$ _____ _____
$25 - 13 =$ _____ _____
$13 + 7 =$ _____ _____
$3 \times 6 =$ _____ _____
$30 \div 2 =$ _____ _____
$21 \times 1 =$ _____ _____
$7 - 5 =$ _____ _____
$7 + 5 =$ _____ _____
$30 \div 6 =$ _____ _____
$14 + 5 =$ _____ _____
$8 - 6 =$ _____ _____
$5 \times 5 =$ _____ _____
$18 - 9 =$ _____ _____
$16 + 6 =$ _____ _____
$8 - 7 =$ _____ _____
$2 \times 7 =$ _____ _____
$40 \div 2 =$ _____ _____
$28 - 7 =$ _____ _____
$21 \div 3 =$ _____ _____
$16 - 1 =$ _____ _____
$4 \times 2 =$ _____ _____
$11 + 4 =$ _____ _____
$26 \div 2 =$ _____ _____
$14 - 9 =$ _____ _____

COLOR BY NUMBERS

8—Yellow
9—Gray
10—Blue
11—Red
12—Green

Solve each problem. Then color each box, using the chart as a guide.

5 +5	7 +3	6 +4	9 +1	8 +2	3 +7	5 +5	3 +7	8 +2	9 +1	4 +6	3 +7	5 +5	2 +8
4 +6	3 +7	8 +2	3 +7	9 +1	4 +6	6 +5	5 +6	3 +7	5 +5	9 +1	10 +0	4 +6	5 +5
5 +5	7 +3	4 +6	8 +2	6 +4	9 +1	7 +4	10 +1	8 +2	3 +7	5 +5	8 +2	7 +3	4 +6
9 +1	3 +7	8 +2	6 +4	9 +1	8 +3	5 +6	9 +2	6 +5	6 +4	7 +3	5 +5	10 +0	8 +2
10 +0	5 +5	4 +6	7 +4	10 +1	6 +5	0 +9	6 +3	11 +0	4 +7	3 +8	3 +7	4 +6	7 +3
1 +9	8 +2	9 +2	4 +7	6 +5	8 +3	2 +9	6 +5	10 +1	2 +9	5 +6	7 +4	8 +2	6 +4
7 +3	6 +4	5 +6	3 +8	5 +4	9 +2	4 +4	5 +3	8 +3	6 +3	9 +2	6 +5	5 +5	9 +1
5 +5	9 +1	11 +0	7 +4	2 +9	10 +1	6 +2	7 +1	6 +5	3 +8	5 +6	4 +7	3 +7	4 +6
9 +3	8 +4	4 +7	10 +1	5 +6	3 +8	0 +8	2 +6	6 +5	2 +9	10 +1	5 +6	7 +5	10 +2
4 +8	6 +6	1 +11	3 +9	5 +7	10 +2	8 +4	7 +5	2 +10	11 +1	8 +4	7 +5	12 +0	6 +6

TO GREAT LENGTHS

The new exhibit at the Dino-Rama is about to open. All we need now is for the curator, Dr. Zena Zoic,

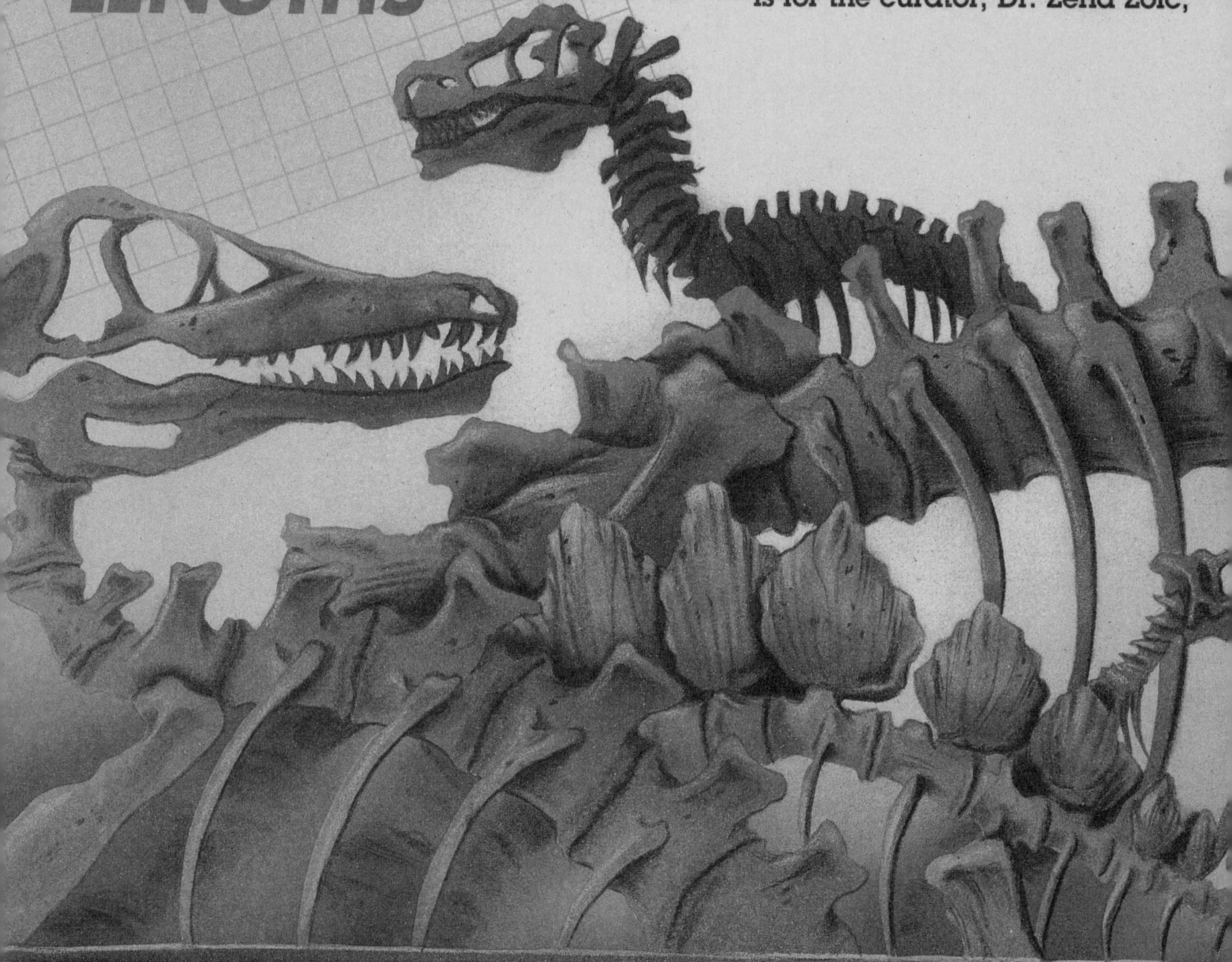

NUMBER OF FEET	9					72
Baryonyx						
Deinonychus						
Mamenchisaurus						
Nanotyrannus						
Plateosaurus						
Stegosaurus						
Tyrannosaurus						

Illustration: Michael Austin

Answer on page 51

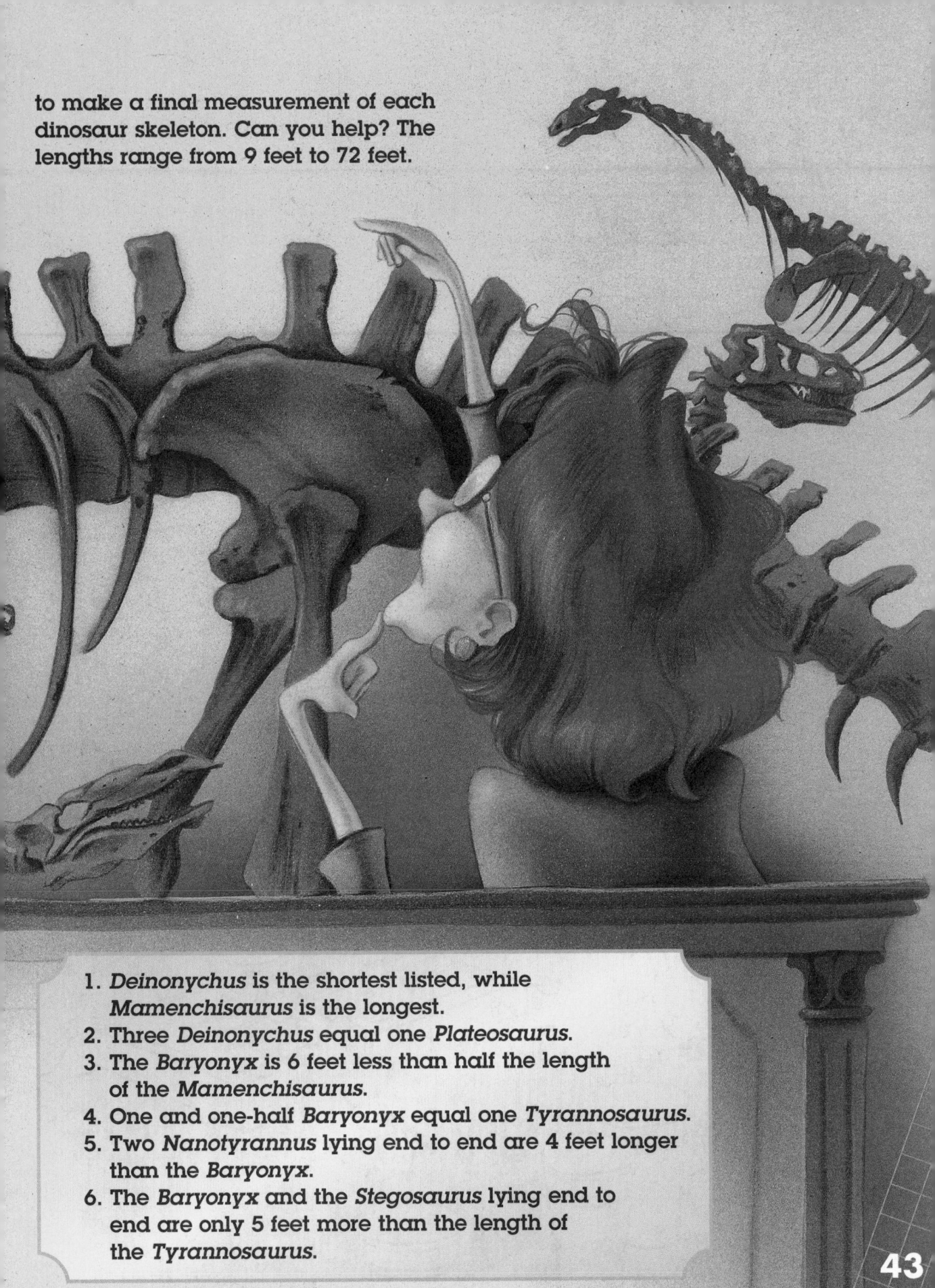

to make a final measurement of each dinosaur skeleton. Can you help? The lengths range from 9 feet to 72 feet.

1. *Deinonychus* is the shortest listed, while *Mamenchisaurus* is the longest.
2. Three *Deinonychus* equal one *Plateosaurus*.
3. The *Baryonyx* is 6 feet less than half the length of the *Mamenchisaurus*.
4. One and one-half *Baryonyx* equal one *Tyrannosaurus*.
5. Two *Nanotyrannus* lying end to end are 4 feet longer than the *Baryonyx*.
6. The *Baryonyx* and the *Stegosaurus* lying end to end are only 5 feet more than the length of the *Tyrannosaurus*.

FOUNTAIN FRENZY

Uh-oh! The soda fountain at Farley's Food Fun House is on the fritz. Five gallons of soda pop are left in the fountain. How many large glasses of soda can Farley serve before he runs out?

MENU

DOGS ——————— $2.00
BURGERS ——————— $3.75
NACHOS ——————— $2.75
FRIES ——————— $1.25

— DRINKS —
Regular = 1 cup $1.50
Large = 1 pint $2.00

Illustration: Bill Colrus

Hint on page 47

WHAT'S THE ANGLE?

Below each blank is a number. Each number marks an angle of degrees from the flat horizon of 0 as shown here. If you can match the right letter with the angle of degrees asked for beneath each blank, you'll be able to answer the riddle and escape this labyrinth.

Illustration: Don Robison

What's the best way to reach a goal if you can't move in a straight line?

$\overline{}$ $\overline{}$ $\overline{}$ $\overline{}$ $\overline{}$ $\overline{}$ $\overline{}$ $\overline{}$ $\overline{}$.
20 155 0   90 180 45 135 70 115

Hint on page 47

Answer on page 51

HINTS AND BRIGHT IDEAS

These hints may help with some of the trickier puzzles.

AUNT ADA (page 6)
The sequence of numbers has nothing to do with the answers. She likes some numbers just because of the way they are spelled.

PAIR SQUARES (page 7)
Number 1 goes in the last cupcake.

DANCING DIGITS (pages 8-9)
Each clue describes one number on the dance floor. Cross off each one as you find it.

FAMILY MATTERS (pages 12-13)
Remember that one child of each set of grandparents is actually Fran's parents.

HOUSE HUNTING (page 14)
Only the northernmost house is northeast of one family and northwest of another family.

TALENT NIGHT (page 22)
If Manuel went on at 8:00, Sylvia would have had to go on at 7:00. The last clue says this is impossible if the show started at 7:00. A boy went on last.

HIDDEN MEASURES (page 23)
The units of measurement include distances, weights, and time. The first five units you're after are inch, acre, ounce, carat, and ton.

CROSSNUMBER (pages 24-25)
There are 2,000 pounds in a ton. The number 10 is perfect in gymnastics. A score is 20.

SNOW PROBLEM (page 26)
Try to figure out the house-lot length first. It's 2 × 100.

SQUARE DIVISION (page 27)
One line will be horizontal, and one will be vertical.
The other two will cross at different angles.

A VINE TIME (pages 28-29)
There are 12 inches in 1 foot. If one leaf equals
6 inches of growth, two leaves equal 12 inches.

ANACROSTIC (pages 32-33)
Look at the words as they come together on the grid.
When you begin to form words, you'll know which letters
go with what numbers. You can use this information to
help you find the words on the list.

SCOUT SALES (page 37)
To find out how much each scout earned,
multiply the number of boxes by the price.
Then add the four prices together.

RHODES TRIP (pages 38-39)
When trying to see how many miles were saved,
you may want to add up the two different routes
to find the difference in mileage. Remember to
double the miles when figuring the round trips.

LIBRARY LAUGHS (page 40)
Remember to consult the books to find
the letter that matches each number.

FOUNTAIN FRENZY (page 44)
There are 2 pints in a quart and 4 quarts
in a gallon.

WHAT'S THE ANGLE? (page 45)
You don't need to measure the exact angle in
most cases. Try to approximate which letter falls
on the angle degree asked for. If 0 is at one end
and 180 is at the other, then 90 must be in the
middle. Now try to figure out which numbers
fall between 0 and 90, and between 90 and 180.

ANSWERS

COVER
Crystal has two rabbits:
one white and one black.

MARKET UP (page 3)
The trucks will arrive in this order:
1. Peter Pachyderm
   Peanut Butter
   5 + 21 = 26
2. Flora's Fresh Fruits
   7 + 20 = 27
3. Eggseptional Eggs
   9 + 19 = 28
4. Superior Cabbages
   11 + 18 = 29
5. What A Bunch! Bananas
   13 + 17 = 30
6. Granny's Grits
   15 + 16 = 31

TWOSOMES (pages 4-5)

AUNT ADA (page 6)
Monday—Aunt Ada likes even numbers.
Tuesday—Aunt Ada likes sequential numbers, but doesn't like numbers that have the same digits.
Wednesday—Aunt Ada likes three-letter numbers.
Thursday—Aunt Ada likes numbers that begin with *E.*
Friday—Aunt Ada likes one-syllable numbers.

PAIR SQUARES (page 7)

DANCING DIGITS (pages 8-9)
A. 11	D. 6	G. 2	J. 7	M. 31
B. 24	E. 49	H. 25	K. 36	N. 1
C. 14	F. 5	I. 63	L. 83	O. 12

CHUCKERS (page 10)
A. 325 pieces
B. 45 pieces per minute
C. 9 minutes

DOTS A LOT (page 11)

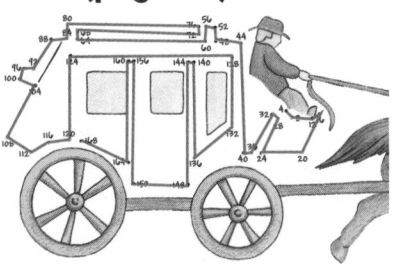

FAMILY MATTERS (pages 12-13)
Grandparents: 4
Parents: 2
Uncles: 2
Aunts: 2
First Cousins: 4
Siblings: 1

HOUSE HUNTING (page 14)
The Clements' place is the center house.

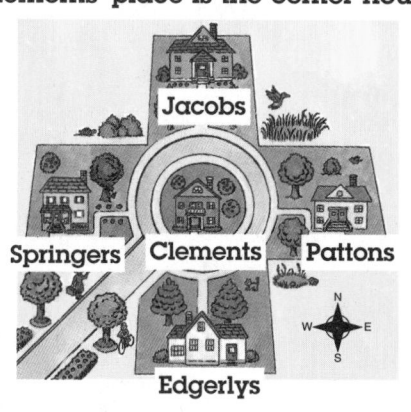

BIRD WORDS (page 15)
ROBIN
BLUE JAY
PARROT
SPARROW
HUMMINGBIRD

Why is the sky so high?
SO BIRDS WON'T BUMP THEIR HEADS

MATH MAZE (pages 16-17)

LISTEN UP (page 18)
HOW CAN A TRAIN HEAR?
BY USING ITS ENGINE-EARS

INDIVISIBLE (page 19)
1. *The* is repeated three times.
2. *To*, *of*, *and*, and *for* are all repeated twice.
3. *Indivisible* has *I* repeated four times.
4. There are no nine-letter words in this statement.
5. Four words begin and end with the same letter: *States*, *stands*, *nation*, *America*.

I pledge allegiance to the flag of the United States of America and to the Republic for which it stands, one nation under God, indivisible, with liberty and justice for all.

SCRAMBLED PICTURE (pages 20-21)

TALENT NIGHT (page 22)
7:00—Gil
7:30—Desiree
8:00—Sylvia
8:30—Tanya
9:00—Manuel

HIDDEN MEASURES (page 23)
1. inch—IN CHina
2. acre—mAC REally
3. ounce—tO UNCErtainly
4. carat—CAR AT
5. ton—TO Notice
6. mile—eMIL Explained
7. yard—mY ARDent
8. pint—uP IN The
9. bushel—BUS HELd
10. furlong—unFURL ON Grand
11. hour—rusH OUR
12. second—worSE CONDition
13. rod—foR ODd
14. gallon—GAL LONg
15. cup—eriC UP

CROSSNUMBER (pages 24-25)

1	7	7	6		3	1
2	2		1	5	2	1
1		1	0	0	0	
5	2				5	5
	5	9	1	0		0
2	0	0	0		1	0
8	0		1	1	0	0

SNOW PROBLEM (page 26)
House lot—200 feet long
Parking lot—700 feet long

SQUARE DIVISION (page 27)
The greatest number of sections you can create is 11.

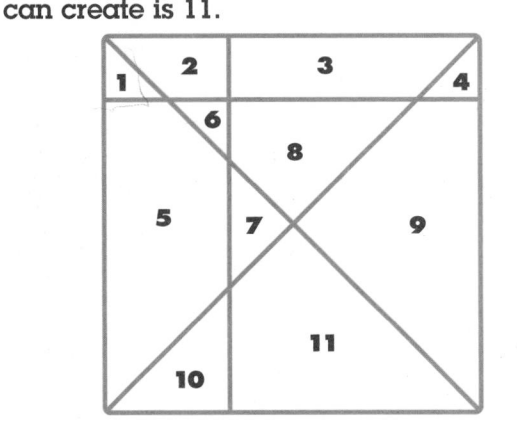

A VINE TIME (pages 28-29)

1. 12 feet (24 leaves)
2. 14 feet (28 leaves)
3. 16 feet (32 leaves)
4. 13 feet (26 leaves)
5. 15 feet (30 leaves)

MATHMAGIC (page 30)

If your friend guesses odd, count the VALUE of the coins, which in this case is $.20. Twenty is an even number. If your friend guesses even, count the NUMBER of coins, which in this case is 7 (her penny and your 6 coins). Seven is an odd number, so she's wrong again.

This trick will work with any odd number of coins that total an even number. It will also work with any even number of coins that total an odd number. As long as you don't let your friend slip in the "wrong" type of coin, you should always win.

PRECISE ICE (page 31)

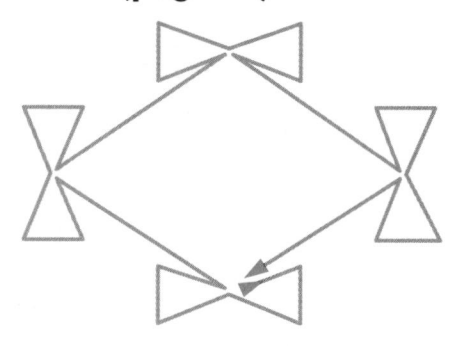

ANACROSTIC (pages 32-33)

A. FOURTEEN
B. SKATE
C. ONE MILLION
D. MUST
E. TWENTY
F. BOSS
G. THIRTY
H. COST
I. TWELVE

I	T		T	A	K	E	S
S	E	V	E	N	T	Y	
–	T	W	O		M	U	S
C	L	E	S		T	O	
F	R	O	W	N		B	U
T		O	N	L	Y		T
H	I	R	T	E	E	N	
T	O		S	M	I	L	E

IT TAKES SEVENTY-TWO MUSCLES TO FROWN BUT ONLY THIRTEEN TO SMILE.

HIDDEN NUMBERS (pages 34-35)

A. 562	J. 19,569	S. 5,000
B. 175	K. 2,112	T. 121
C. 825	L. 3,636	U. 3,708
D. 3,752	M. 248	V. 731
E. 1,250	N. 150	W. 8,570
F. 243	O. 2,000	X. 5,109
G. 10,810	P. 1,954	Y. 1,707
H. 3,500	Q. 101,995	Z. 6,238
I. 555	R. 8,095	

SIMILAR CIRCLES (page 36)

All the circles but one have 8 sections. D has 9 sections.

SCOUT SALES (page 37)

Aleesha sold 43 boxes. Total: $125.25
Bethany sold 40 boxes. Total: $115.75
Caitlin sold 42 boxes. Total: $121.00
Deandra sold 44 boxes. Total: $121.50

Aleesha earned the most money at $125.25. Deandra sold the most boxes at 44.

RHODES TRIP (pages 38-39)

1. They planned to travel 6,490 miles. One way from Tampa to Seattle is 3,245 miles.
2. It took 7 hours from Tampa to Atlanta.
3. It would have added 302 extra miles. One way is 151 miles.
4. The trip would have been 4,148 miles shorter. It is 2,342 miles round trip from Tampa to Chicago, so 6,490 - 2,342 = 4,148.
5. It cost $45.15 (860 ÷ 20 = 43 gallons; 43 × $1.05 = $45.15).
6. They arrived at 2:00 p.m. (256 miles ÷ 64 = 4 hours).
7. They saved 2,750 miles (554 + 821 = 1,375 × 2 = 2,750).